This book belongs to:

_____

D1532146

I'm Dreaming of a Brown Christmas
Copyright © 2021 by Steven T. Gray and Vernon D Gibbs II
Cuzzos Publishing and Media™ All rights reserved.

This book or any portion thereof may not be reproduced or used in any manner whatsoever without the express
written permission of the publisher except for the use of brief quotations in a book review.
I'm Dreaming of a Brown Christmas is a work of fiction. Characters and incidents are the products of the author's
imagination. Any resemblance to actual persons, living or dead, or actual events is purely coincidental.

Cuzzos Publishing and Media
P.O. Box 84
New Milford, NJ 07646

Ordering Information:
Special discounts are available on large quantity purchases by not-for-profit organizations, associations, and others.

For details contact:
Cuzzos Publishing and Media at cuzzospublishingandmedia@gmail.com
Orders by U.S. trade bookstores and wholesalers can contact the same email above.
First Edition, First Printing, 2021

Resource Attribution: Portions of this book have been designed using resources from
vecteezy.com, shutterstock.com, clipartpng.com, classroomclipart.com

Thank you to all the friends and family who helped bring this book to life.
We could not have done this without your comments, ideas, critiques and continued support!

Isaiah 9:6 KJV
6 For unto us a child is born, unto us a son is given: and the government shall be upon his shoulder: and his name
shall be called Wonderful, Counsellor, The mighty God, The everlasting Father, The Prince of Peace.

I'm Dreaming of A Brown Christmas

By Steven T. Gray and Vernon D. Gibbs

A
CUZZOS
BOOK

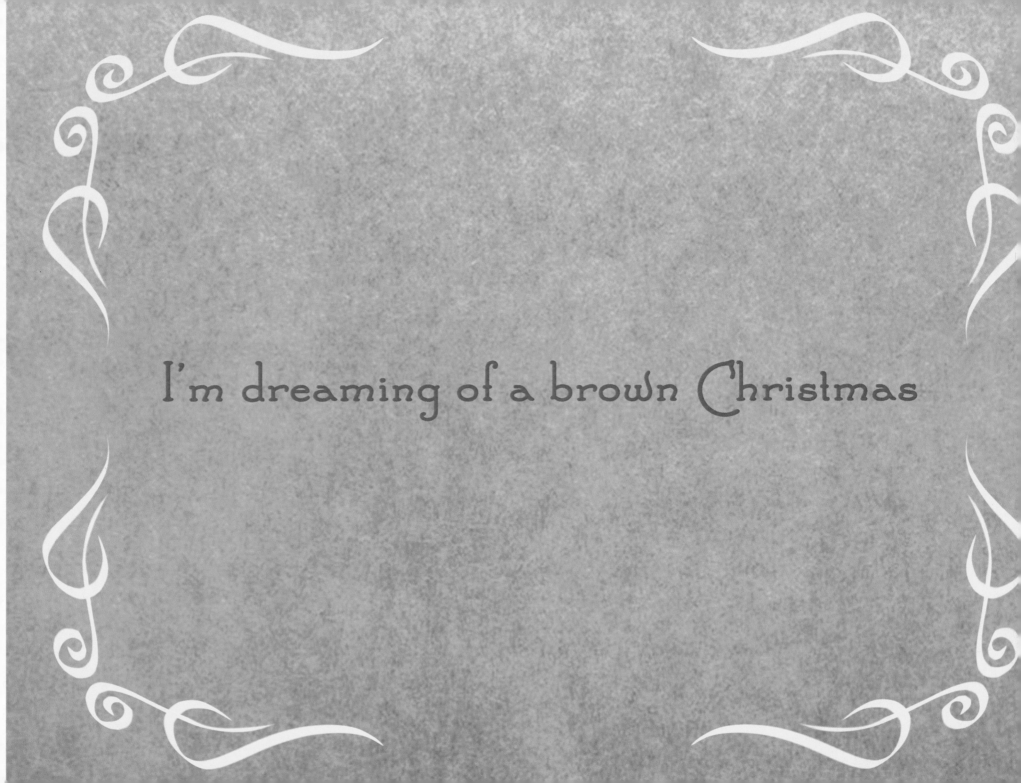

I'm dreaming of a brown Christmas

With every lit brownstone window

In their cozy spaces

Brown smiling faces

Glad to come in

Out of the snow

I'm dreaming of a
Brown Christmas
Loved ones of all shades
Come around
Hugs and kisses
Blessed, safe and sound
In my dreams
Christmas is white and brown

I'm dreaming of a
Brown Christmas
Hot cocoa and
Christmas cookies

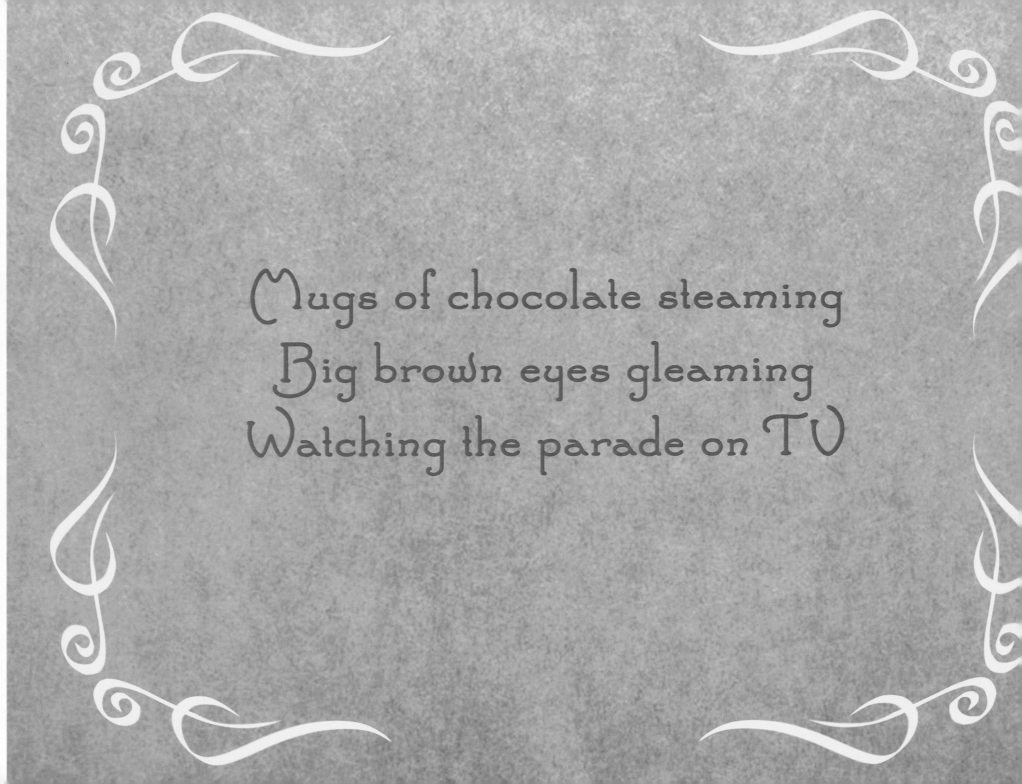

Mugs of chocolate steaming
Big brown eyes gleaming
Watching the parade on TV

I'm dreaming of a
Brown Christmas
Loved ones of all shades
Come around
Hugs and kisses
Blessed, safe and sound
In my dreams
Christmas is white and brown

I'm dreaming of a
Brown Christmas
Mom roasting the
Big brown turkey
With gravy and stuffing

...while Dad's adjusting

The brown-skinned

Angel on our tree

I'm dreaming of a

Brown Christmas

Loved ones of all shades

Come around

Hugs and kisses

Blessed, safe and sound

In my dreams

Christmas is white and brown

I'm dreaming of a
Brown Christmas
Our soldier's home
From overseas
In her brown uniform
Came through a snow storm
To be with us on Christmas Eve

I'm dreaming of a

Brown Christmas

Loved ones of all shades

Come around

Hugs and kisses

Blessed, safe and sound

In my dreams

Christmas is white and brown

I'm dreaming of a
Brown Christmas
The kids at church
Put on their play

In their red attire

The gospel choir

Wish Jesus a

Happy Birthday

I'm dreaming of a
Brown Christmas
Loved ones of all shades
Come around
Hugs and kisses
Blessed, safe and sound
In my dreams
Christmas is white and brown

About the Creators

Steven T. Gray is a visual artist, illustrator, sculptor, producer and musician born in Brooklyn, NY and raised in Queens, NY. He attended the School of Art & Design in Manhattan, NY.

As a teenager he was signed to Capitol records as a part of a vocal group and recorded two top ten songs. He then went on to work with several well known musical artists and produced and performed national television commercials.

He currently lives in North Carolina with his wife Christina. They have two daughters, Jasmine and Nia. Jasmine and her husband Vernte recently had their first child, Xavier.

Proverbs 3:5-6 Trust in the Lord with all your heart and lean not on your own understanding; in all your ways submit to Him, and He will make your paths straight.

Vernon D. Gibbs II has been a stay-at-home dad since 2015. Previously, he worked in marketing and most recently held a position at his alma mater Columbia University, where he earned his BA in Architecture in 2000.

He and his wife Tresha, an MD in child mental health live in New Jersey with their three children, 5-year-old twins Jackson and Sophia and their 8-year-old son Justin.

"I'm Dreaming of a Brown Christmas" is the second book that he has co-written with his cousin Steve. Their first book, "When Good Fruit Goes Bad" is about eating healthy, creating less food waste, and knowing that you have value. You can follow Vernon on social media as coolminivandad.

Follow Cuzzos on
Instagram @cuzzosmedia
https://www.facebook.com/cuzzospublishingandmedia/

CPSIA information can be obtained
at www.ICGtesting.com
Printed in the USA
BVRC101024231221
624743BV00017B/13